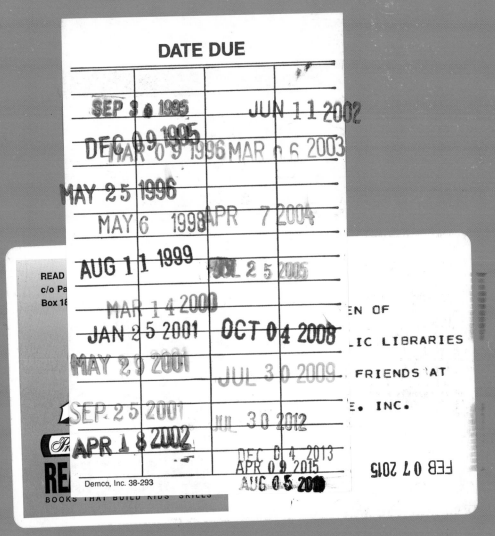

BLACKIE CHILDREN'S BOOKS
Published by the Penguin Group
Penguin Books Ltd, 27 Wrights Lane, London W8 5TZ, England
Penguin Books USA Inc., 375 Hudson Street, New York, New York 10014, USA
Penguin Books Australia Ltd, Ringwood, Victoria, Australia
Penguin Books Canada Ltd, 10 Alcorn Avenue, Toronto, Ontario, Canada M4V 3B2
Penguin Books (NZ) Ltd, 182 – 190 Wairau Road, Auckland 10, New Zealand

Penguin Books Ltd, Registered Offices: Harmondsworth, Middlesex, England

First published 1992
10 9 8 7 6 5 4 3 2 1

Text and illustrations copyright© Victor Ambrus, 1992

The moral right of the author/illustrator has been asserted

Printed in Hong Kong

A CIP catalogue record for this book is available from the British Library
ISBN 0 216 93253 X

First American edition published 1992 by
Peter Bedrick Books, 2112 Broadway, New York, NY 10023

Library of Congress Cataloging-in-Publication Data is available for this title
ISBN 0 87226 465 3

FOLK TALES OF THE WORLD

NEVER LAUGH AT BEARS

A Transylvanian Folk Tale

Victor Ambrus

Blackie
London

Bedrick/Blackie
New York

A long way from here, near the high Carpathian Mountains, lived a poor woodcutter. He had a wife, three children, one cow and a few hens.

One morning, the woodcutter took his cow to the edge of the forest to plough his field. As he was working, he heard a lot of growling and squeaking coming from the forest. He went to investigate and what did he see?

A big brown bear was having a fight with a
little grey rabbit. Every time the bear swung
a punch, the little rabbit hopped out of the way!
The woodcutter burst out laughing. He laughed
so much that he fell to the ground clutching
his stomach.

The bear was furious at being laughed at. He turned on the woodcutter and growled, 'What's so funny, you miserable woodcutter?'

'Forgive me, Mr Bear, sir, but I could not stop myself from laughing, seeing such a handsome, grand animal as yourself, fighting a little slip of a rabbit,' stammered the woodcutter.

'Very well, poor man, you will regret this for the rest of your life! I am going to eat your cow for my supper and I may even have *you* for afters!'

The woodcutter took fright at this and started to plead with the bear.

'Oh, Mr Bear, please don't eat my cow until after sunset. First let me finish ploughing the field so I can sow some seed for next year. Then my wife and three children will have something to eat!'

'As you've asked me nicely,' answered the bear, 'I will leave you alone until after sunset, but you had better hurry because I am getting really hungry.'

The poor woodcutter started ploughing the field
and then sat down to eat his lunch. He didn't have
much of an appetite. As he sat there holding his
head in his hands, who should come along, but
a cunning fox.

'What's upsetting you so much, my friend?'
he asked the woodcutter. 'Don't even ask me, Fox,'
he replied. 'I am very sad because the bear is coming
to eat my cow at sunset, and may even have *me*
for afters!'

'Is that all? If you promise me a treat, I might be
able to help you,' murmured the fox.

'What have I got, that you would want, Fox?' asked the
woodcutter.

'If you've got a cow,' said the wily fox, 'you may well have a few hens to go with it. I'm not greedy, so if you give me six fat hens and a cockerel, I will save you from the bear. Listen out for the hunting horn when I go into the forest and see what a fright the bear will get!'

'Very well,' sighed the woodcutter as the fox scampered away.

The woodcutter pondered. He didn't want to lose his cow to the bear, but if he lost all his hens to the fox there would be no eggs for the family to eat. He thought hard, and then quickly fetched a large coal sack from his house and carried on ploughing. He had nearly finished when the big brown bear arrived.

'Let's have your cow then' said the bear
hungrily.

Just then the fox began trumpeting away
in the forest.

'What's that noise?' asked the worried bear.

'Oh, it's just those hunters blowing their
horns again,' said the woodcutter.

'Quick, hide me somewhere,' cried the bear,
shaking with fright, 'If you save me you can
keep your cow!'

'Jump into the sack and don't make a sound,'
said the woodcutter. The bear did as he was
told, and the woodcutter tied the coal sack
with strong rope, and took it back to his house.

A little later, the fox trotted purposefully into
the woodcutter's yard.
'What's in the bag?' he demanded in a big voice.

'Your hens and your cockerel,' whispered the woodcutter, 'and as your plan worked so well I put in a few extra hens. Just take it away quickly before the bear comes back!'

The fox eagerly dragged away the heavy sack,
through bushes and trees, right into the middle
of the forest. He opened it up and out popped
the bear, covered in bumps, bruises and
coal dust!

He lashed out at the fox in a rage, but the fox jumped out of the way, as quick as lightning. For all I know they are still fighting!

The woodcutter went home to his wife and three children and they had a big pot of goulash to celebrate!

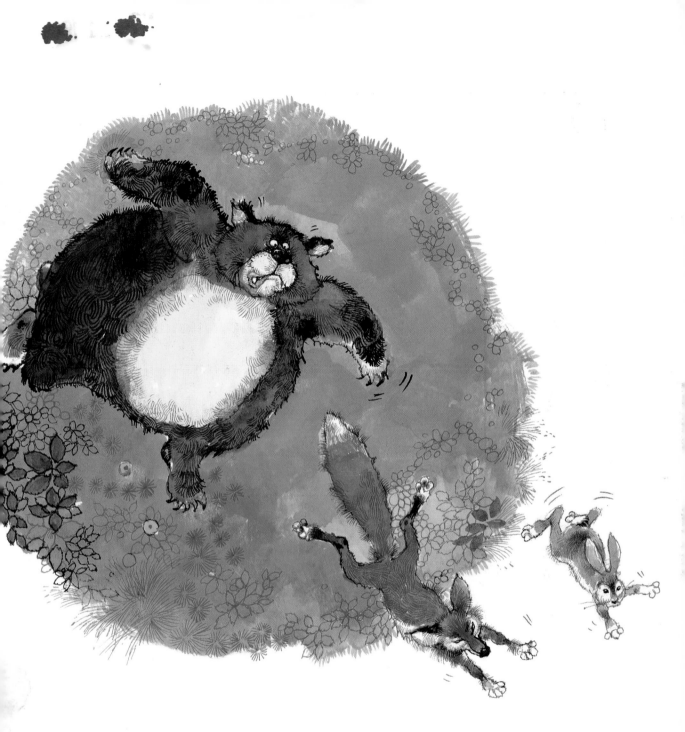

If you ever go near a forest and see a big, brown bear chasing a little red fox, or a little grey rabbit, whatever you do, don't laugh. Bears don't like it!